Mighty Mighty MONSTERS
Lost in
SPOOKY FOREST

created by Sean O'Reilly
illustrated by Arcana Studio

Raintree

www.raintreepublishers.co.uk
Visit our website to find out
more information about
Raintree books.

To order:
☎ Phone 0845 6044371
📄 Fax +44 (0) 1865 312263
✉ Email myorders@raintreepublishers.co.uk

Customers from outside the UK please telephone +44 1865 312262

Raintree is an imprint of Capstone Global Library Limited,
a company incorporated in England and Wales having its registered
office at 7 Pilgrim Street, London, EC4V 6LB
– Registered company number: 6695582

First published by Stone Arch Books in 2010
First published in the United Kingdom in paperback in 2012
The moral rights of the proprietor have been asserted.

Edited by Laura Knowles
Originated by Capstone Global Library Ltd
Printed and bound in China by South China Printing Company

ISBN 978 1 406 23720 7 (paperback)
16 15 14 13 12
10 9 8 7 6 5 4 3 2 1

British Library Cataloguing in Publication Data
A full catalogue record for this book is available
from the British Library.

In a strange corner of the world known as Transylmania . . .

Legendary monsters were born.

WELCOME TO TRANSYLMANIA

But long before their frightful fame, these classic creatures faced fears of their own.

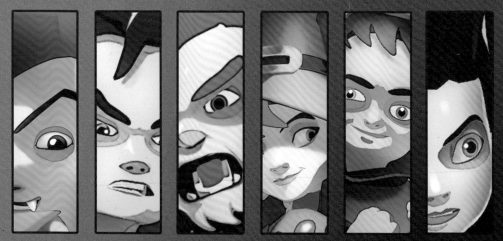

To take on terrifying teachers and homework horrors, they formed the most fearsome friendship on Earth . . .

Mighty Mighty MONSTERS

Vlad

Talbot

Witchita

Milton

Poto

Frankie

Igor

Mary

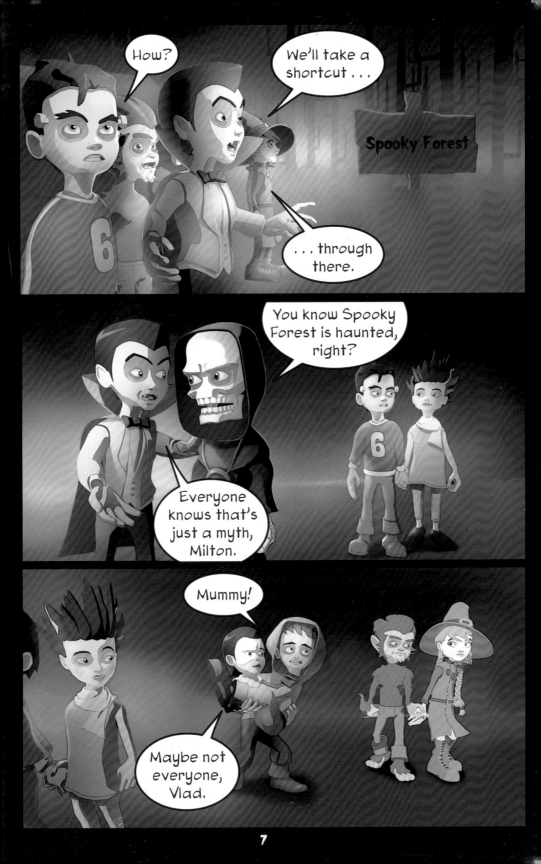

Whew! That was close!
A little too close, I'd say.
Yeah, I have a bad feeling about this place.
Hey, guys, something's wrong with Igor.
zZzZZ
Tell him to hang in there, Poto.
I think I smell the school's canteen!

Thanks, Witchita. But once everyone gets warm, we have to keep moving.
Something isn't right. I've never been this sleepy before.
Yeah, my feet are killing me.
I hear ya, dude. I'm bone-tired.

The trolls of this forest have cast a spell over us all, Frankie.

That doesn't sound good.

Yeah, but Witchita can stop any spell. Right?

Not this one, Vlad. It's too powerful.

Oh.

Don't worry, Witchita. We'll help you.

He's right!

No silly little troll spell is going to spook the Mighty Mighty Monsters!

Meanwhile, in another part of the forest . . .
Where are you, Witchita?

31

We're celebrating school.
Creak!
Well, I guess anything is better than that spooky forest.

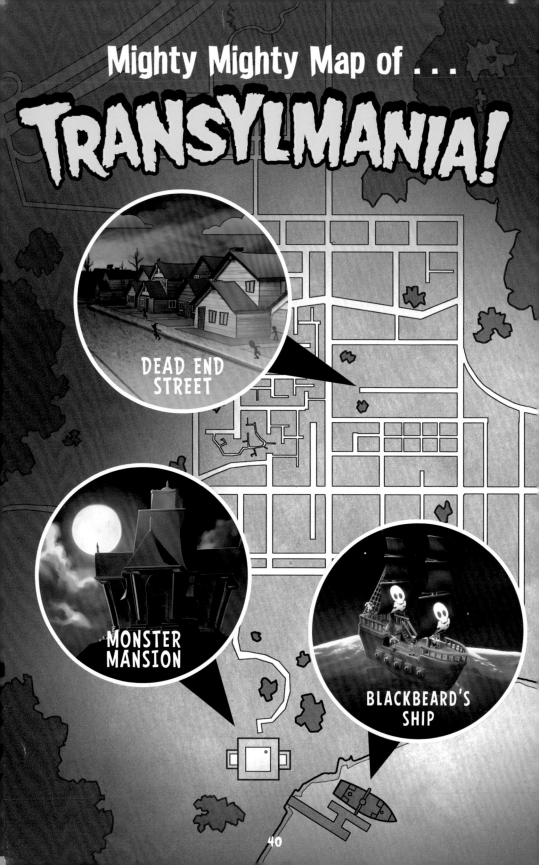

SPOOKY
FOREST

MONSTER
SCHOOL

FLAME OF
HALLOWEEN

CASTLE OF
DOOM

Mighty Mighty
MONSTERS

...BEFORE THEY WERE STARS!

TALBOT

Nickname: Wolfie

Hometown: Transylmania

Favourite colour: brown (like his fur)

Favourite animal: anything but cats

Mighty mighty powers:
shape-shifting, or the ability to
transform into a wolf; super-scent;
super-hearing; loyalty.

BIOGRAPHY

Unlike the other Mighty Mighty Monsters, Talbot's inner
beast only comes out during a full moon. Luckily, in the
terrifying town of Transylmania, the moon is ALWAYS full.
With super-hearing and a powerful nose, Talbot is the
gang's best tracker. And, much like his canine cousins, the
furry beast is the most loyal of friends. After starring in
a number of classic movies, Talbot has become one of the
creepiest creatures of all time — a monster icon.

WHERE ARE THEY NOW?

Legends of real-life werewolves have been around for thousands of years. In fact, one of the first werewolf stories appears in Greek mythology.

The werewolf became a big-screen hit when *The Wolfman* film premiered in 1941. Lon Chaney, Jr. starred as the fearsome furball in the film.

Many movies, books, and plays have been written about werewolves since the 1941 film. Most recently, in 2010, Benicio del Toro starred as the Wolfman in a remake of the classic monster film.

ABOUT SEAN O'REILLY
AND ARCANA STUDIO

As a lifelong comics fan, Sean O'Reilly dreamed of becoming a comic book creator. In 2004, he realized that dream by creating Arcana Studio. In one short year, O'Reilly took his studio from a one-person operation in his house to an award-winning comic book publisher with more than 150 graphic novels produced for Harper Collins, Simon & Schuster, Random House, Scholastic, and others.

Within a year, the company won many awards including the Shuster Award for Outstanding Publisher and the Moonbeam Award for top children's graphic novel. O'Reilly also won the Top 40 Under 40 award from the city of Vancouver and authored The Clockwork Girl for Top Graphic Novel at Book Expo America in 2009.

Currently, O'Reilly is one of the most prolific independent comic book writers in Canada. While showing no signs of slowing down in comics, he now also writes screenplays and adapts his creations for the big screen.

GLOSSARY

canteen self-service restaurant or the area lunch is served in school

celebrating doing something enjoyable to honour a special occasion

introduce tell the name of one person to another person

kidnapped captured and taken illegally by another person

myth false idea that many people believe

shortcut route that is faster and more direct than the usual route

spooky creepy or scary

starving suffering or dying from a lack of food

troll creature in fairy tales that lives in caves or under bridges

DISCUSSION QUESTIONS

1. The Mighty Mighty Monsters are a team. Do you think they have a leader? If so, which monster do you think is the leader? Why?

2. Even the mightiest monsters get scared. What are a few things that you're scared of? How do you overcome your fears?

3. All of the Mighty Mighty Monsters are different. Which character do you like the best and why?

WRITING PROMPTS

1. Write about the creepiest, crawliest place you've ever been. Was it a haunted house? A spooky forest? Describe.

2. Write a story about your own group of friends. What kind of adventures do you have? What do you do for fun?

3. Write your own Mighty Mighty Monsters adventure. What will the ghoulish gang do next? What villains will they face? You decide.

FIND OUT MORE

INFORMATION BOOKS

Ghosts and Other Spectres (Dark Side), Anita
Ganeri (Wayland, 2010)

The Mystery of Vampires and Werewolves
(Can Science Solve?), Chris Oxlade (Heinemann
Library, 2008)

GRAPHIC NOVELS

Dracula (Graphic Revolve), Bram Stoker, retold by
Michael Burgan (Raintree, 2009)

Frankenstein (Graphic Revolve), Mary Shelley, retold
by Michael Burgan (Raintree, 2009)

Werewolf (Graphic Chillers), Jeff Zornow (Franklin
Watts, 2010)

WEBSITE

learnenglishkids.britishcouncil.org/en/make-
your-own/make-your-monster
Visit this website to create your own monster. You
can also invent your own scary story, dangerous
animal, or superhero.

Mighty Mighty MONSTERS ADVENTURES

Monster Mansion
ISBN: 978 1 406 23721 4

New Monster in School
ISBN: 978 1 406 23723 8

Hide and Shriek
ISBN: 978 1 406 23718 4

The King of Halloween Castle
ISBN: 978 1 406 23719 1

My Missing Monster
ISBN: 978 1 406 23722 1